Tea FOR Ruby

by

SARAH FERGUSON
THE DUCHESS OF YORK

illustrated by
ROBIN PREISS GLASSER

SCHOLASTIC INC.
New York Toronto London Auckland
Sydney Mexico City New Delhi Hong Kong

To Beatrice and Eugenie—
you make my world complete
—S. F.

For Jacqueline Preiss Weitzman—
my sister, my partner, my friend
—R. P. G.

ISBN 978-0-545-23826-7

Text copyright © 2008 by Sarah Ferguson, The Duchess of York.
Illustrations copyright © 2008 by Robin Preiss Glasser. All rights reserved. Published by Scholastic Inc., 557 Broadway, New York, NY 10012, by arrangement with Simon & Schuster Books for Young Readers, an imprint of Simon & Schuster Children's Publishing Division. SCHOLASTIC and associated logos are trademarks and/or registered trademarks of Scholastic Inc.

12 11 10 9 8 7 6 5 4 3 2 1   10 11 12 13 14 15/0

Printed in the U.S.A.   08

This edition first printing, January 2010

Book design by Dan Potash
The text for this book is set in Fiddlestix.
The illustrations for this book are rendered in ink, watercolor, and colored pencil.

You are invited
to have tea with
The Queen
on Sunday.

Please bring your very best manners.

"The Queen."

"The Queen."

"I've been invited to have tea with the Queen!"

"Ruby, I hope you will
dress appropriately
when you have tea with . . .
 **the Queen**."

"I've been invited to have tea with the Queen!"

MR. ROY'S PUPPET FARM

"Ruby, I hope you won't talk when you shouldn't when you have tea with . . .

the Queen."

"The Queen."

"Ruby, I hope you won't talk with your mouth full and won't tip your chair back and will use your fork and napkin when you have tea with . . .

The Queen."

"Tomorrow I'm having tea with the Queen!"

"Ruby, I hope you'll remember to sit up straight when you have tea with the Queen."

Today's the day!

"Let's hurry so we won't be late!"

Remember to chew with my mouth closed.

Remember not to speak with my mouth full.

Remember to say "please" and "thank you."

Remember to welcome people.

Remember to use my fork and napkin.

Remember not to interrupt.

Remember not to shout.

Remember to wait my turn.

Remember to sit up straight.

Remember not to talk when I shouldn't.

"GRANDMA?"

"May I offer you more tea, Princess Ruby?"

"Oh, yes, please, Grandma. Thank you."